KU-331-490

THE VICTORIANA COLLECTION

BIRTHDAY BOOK

THE VICTORIANA COLLECTION

BIRTHDAY BOOK

CENTURY BENHAM
LONDON SYDNEY AUCKLAND JOHANNESBURG

FIRST PUBLISHED IN GREAT BRITAIN IN 1990
BY CENTURY BENHAM LTD
CENTURY HUTCHINSON PUBLISHING GROUP
20 VAUXHALL BRIDGE ROAD
LONDON SW1V 2SA

COPYRIGHT © CENTURY BENHAM LTD 1990
ILLUSTRATIONS COPYRIGHT © MADAME TUSSAUD'S 1990

ALL RIGHTS RESERVED. NO PART OF THIS BOOK MAY BE REPRODUCED IN ANY FORM
OR BY ANY MEANS WITHOUT PERMISSION IN WRITING FROM THE PUBLISHER

SET IN COPPERPLATE GOTHIC
BY FMT GRAPHICS LIMITED, SOUTHWARK, LONDON
PRINTED AND BOUND IN SINGAPORE

ISBN 0 7126 37044

Introduction

Scraps, reliefs, die-cuts, and chromos all refer to the small pictures of embossed coloured paper which were so popular from the 1880s until the turn of the century, and which were used to decorate all manner of objects inside and outside the home.

From about 1800 every young lady, and many young gentlemen, had a scrap book into which were pasted or copied poems, sketches in pencil and watercolour, cuttings from newspapers or other decorative materials, and 'scraps'. Early scraps took the form of engraved or lithographed sketches, sometimes hand-coloured, and usually depicting rural or comic scenes. But with the advent of improved technology came the chromolithograph cut-outs that we know today as 'scraps'.

The skill of the lithographer was vital to the vibrant but subtle quality of the finished item, since up to twenty colours might be used, each requiring a separate drawing to be made from the original artwork. A design of anything from four to forty repeats would be printed on a single sheet, or swag. After printing, the coloured sheet was coated with a glue-based film to prevent the paper from cracking during the embossing process which followed. Sometimes a sheet of gold film would be added at this stage to give an extra dimension of richness; and the sheet was finally transferred to the stamping press to remove all blank areas.

The subjects used for the scrap sheets are almost limitless: all manner of flora and fauna, children and fashionable ladies, famous people, historic events and buildings, entertainments, and people and animals from the exotic lands of the

EMPIRE. AS THE FASHION FOR COLLECTING THEM GREW, MORE 'NOVELTY' LINES WERE INTRODUCED. SOME SCRAPS WERE BIG ENOUGH TO FILL A WHOLE PAGE OF AN ALBUM. OTHERS COULD BE FOLDED OUT, OR CONSTRUCTED AT HOME, TO GIVE A THREE-DIMENSIONAL FIGURE OR SCENE. IN THE HOME, SCRAPS WERE APPLIED TO MANY HOUSEHOLD ITEMS, BUT ESPECIALLY SCREENS.

THE COMMERCIAL WORLD WAS QUICK TO ADOPT THE APPLICATION PRINCIPLE, ESPECIALLY THE FANCY BOX AND PAPER TRADE. IN GERMANY THEY WERE USED EXTENSIVELY ON BAKERY PRODUCTS. EVEN TODAY FATHER CHRISTMAS FIGURES ARE STILL COMMONLY FOUND ON GINGERBREAD. CARD MANUFACTURERS USED THEM ON VALENTINES, AND LATER ON CHRISTMAS CARDS; AND IN AMERICA THERE WAS A FASHION FOR VISITING CARDS ON WHICH THE OWNER'S NAME, OR A MESSAGE, COULD BE PRINTED BENEATH A HINGED SCRAP IN THE FORM OF A DOVE, OR A HAND. SCRAPS PLAYED A PART IN EARLY ADVERTISING TOO, APPEARING ON POINT-OF-SALE DISPLAYS, TRADE CARDS, ADVERTISING CALENDARS, AND OTHER GIVE-AWAY ITEMS.

THE RISE OF THE CIGARETTE CARD AND THE PICTURE POSTCARD, AND THE CHANGE IN SOCIAL HABITS BROUGHT ABOUT BY ECONOMIC DEPRESSION AND WAR, CONTRIBUTED TO THE DECLINE OF THE SCRAP. ITS HEYDAY WAS FROM 1870 TO 1900, AND IT IS FROM THIS PERIOD THAT ALL THE DESIGNS IN THIS BOOK ARE REPRODUCED, FROM THE COLLECTION OF MADAME TUSSAUD'S.

UNDINE CONCANNON
ARCHIVIST, MADAME TUSSAUD'S

MADAME TUSSAUD'S

MADAME TUSSAUD, BORN IN 1761 IN STRASBOURG, WAS RAISED AND TAUGHT BY HER UNCLE, PHILIPPE CURTIUS, A WAX MODELLER IN PARIS. SHE CAME TO ENGLAND IN 1802 WITH HIS COLLECTION OF FIGURES, WHICH SHE HAD INHERITED, AND FOR THIRTY-THREE YEARS TRAVELLED ALL OVER THE BRITISH ISLES, FINALLY SETTLING IN BAKER STREET. FIVE FURTHER GENERATIONS OF TUSSAUDS RAN THE EXHIBITION, WHICH MOVED IN 1884 TO THE SITE IN MARYLEBONE ROAD, WHERE IT HAS REMAINED EVER SINCE.

JANUARY

JANUARY

1
2
3
4
5
6
7

JANUARY

8

9

10

11

12

13

14

JANUARY

15

16

17

18

19

20

21

JANUARY

22

23

24

25

26

27

28

JANUARY

29
30
31

FEBRUARY

FEBRUARY

1

2

3

4

5

6

7

FEBRUARY

8

9

10

11

12

13

14

FEBRUARY

15

16

17

18

19

20

21

FEBRUARY

22

23

24

25

26

27

28

FEBRUARY

29

MARCH

MARCH

1

2

3

4

5

6

7

MARCH

8

9

10

11

12

13

14

MARCH

15

16

17

18

19

20

21

MARCH

22

23

24

25

26

27

28

MARCH

29

30

31

APRIL

APRIL

1

Dusky

2

3

4

5

6

7

APRIL

8

9

10

11

12

13

14

APRIL

15

16

17

18

19

20

21

APRIL

22

23

24

25

26

27

28

APRIL

29
30

MAY

MAY

1

2

3

4

5

6

7

MAY

8

9

10

11

12

13

14

MAY

15
16
17
Justin Green wood
18
19
20
21

MAY

22

23

24

25

26

Lucy Smith

27

28

MAY

29

30

31

JUNE

JUNE

1

2

3

4

5

6

7

JUNE

8

9

10

11

12

13

14

JUNE

15

16

17

18

19

20

21

JUNE

22

23

24

25

26

27

28

JUNE

29

30

JULY

JULY

1
2
3
4
5
6
7

JULY

8

9

10

11

12

13

14

JULY

15

16

17

18

19

20

21

JULY

22

23

24

25

26

27

28

JULY

29
30
31

AUGUST

AUGUST

1

2

3

4

5

6

7

AUGUST

8

9

10

11

12

13

14

AUGUST

15

16

17

18

19

20

21

AUGUST

22

23

24

25

26

27

28

AUGUST

29
30
31

SEPTEMBER

SEPTEMBER

1

2

3

4

5

6

7

SEPTEMBER

8

9

10

11

12

13

14

SEPTEMBER

15

16

17

18

19

20

21

SEPTEMBER

22

23

24

25

26

27

28

SEPTEMBER

29

30

OCTOBER

OCTOBER

1

2

3

4

5

6

7

OCTOBER

8

9

10

11

12

13

14

OCTOBER

15

16

17

18

19

20

21

OCTOBER

22

23

24

25

26

27

28

OCTOBER

29
30
31

NOVEMBER

NOVEMBER

1

2

3

4

5

6

7

NOVEMBER

8

9

10

11

12

13

14

November

15

16

17

18

19

20

21

NOVEMBER

22

23

24

25

26

27

28

NOVEMBER

29

30

DECEMBER

DECEMBER

1

2

3

4

5

6

7

DECEMBER

8

9

10

11

12

13

14

December

15

16

17

18

19

20

21

DECEMBER

22

23

24

25

26

27

28

DECEMBER

29
30
31